Get set for the new KS2 SATS with CGP!

This CGP book is packed with short, sharp KS2 Maths tests
— it's a brilliant way to help children prepare for the
new Maths SATS in 2016 and beyond.

We've made sure the tests are just like mini versions
of the real SATS, including new Arithmetic Tests that
match the latest curriculum perfectly.

Plus — all the answers are included in a cut-out-and-keep section!

What CGP is all about

Our sole aim here at CGP is to produce the highest quality books
— carefully written, immaculately presented and
dangerously close to being funny.

Then we work our socks off to get them out to you
— at the cheapest possible prices.

Contents

Set C

Just like in the real tests, calculators are not allowed.

Published by CGP

Editors: Shaun Harrogate, Caley Simpson

Contributor: Sue Foord

With thanks to Simon Little and Jonathan Wray for the proofreading.

ISBN: 978 1 78294 240 5

Clipart from Corel®

Printed by Elanders Ltd, Newcastle upon Tyne.

Based on the classic CGP style created by Richard Parsons.

Photocopying this book is not permitted. Extra copies are available from CGP with next day delivery.

0800 1712 712 • www.cgpbooks.co.uk

There are **9 questions** in this test. Give yourself **10 minutes** to answer them all.

1. Fill in the missing digits to make this calculation correct.

$$2\boxed{} + \boxed{}6 = 100$$

_____
1 mark

2. Shade in 3 squares to make the diagram symmetrical about the mirror line.

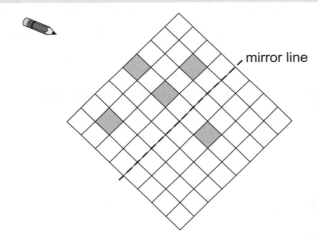

mirror line

_____
1 mark

3. Work out each of these calculations.

$$900 \times 4 = \boxed{}$$

$$560 \div 8 = \boxed{}$$

_____
1 mark

4. Emily needs to weigh a parcel before she posts it.

    What is the weight of Emily's parcel?

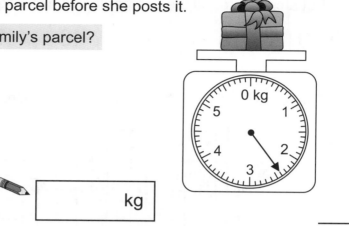

    kg

5. This table shows the activities chosen by children
    at the local leisure centre over three days last week.

	Friday	Saturday	Sunday
Swimming	23	25	19
Climbing wall	8	17	16
Trampolining	9	12	7

    How many children chose the climbing wall during the three days?

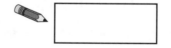

6. Round each decimal to the nearest whole number.

    4.05

    8.52

    16.79

3

7. Put a circle around the number that is **not** a square number.

9   16   36   48   81   100

_____
1 mark

8. The following bar chart shows James and Corey's exam results.

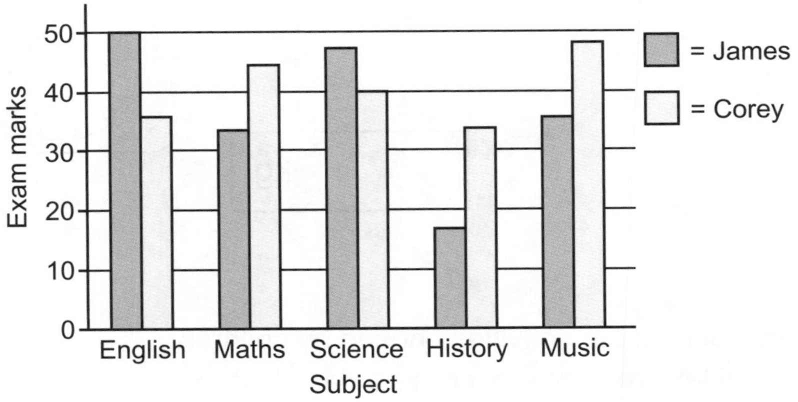

In which two subjects did James get a higher score than Corey?

[   ] and [   ]

_____
1 mark

9. A pond is 36 m long. A duck swims 4 lengths of the pond each day.

How far does the duck swim in **four weeks**?

Show your working. You may get a mark.

[   ] m

_____
2 marks

END OF TEST

[   ] / 10

There are **7 questions** in this test. Give yourself **10 minutes** to answer them all.

1. Put a tick (✓) in the boxes below all of the shapes that have **more than one** right angle.

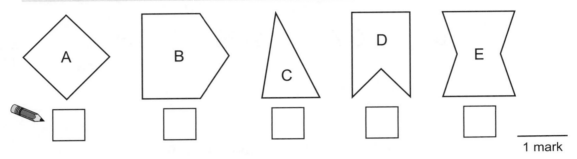

☐   ☐   ☐   ☐   ☐ _____

1 mark

2. Corey needs a new school uniform.

School Uniform Prices	
Blazer	£21.00
Shirt	£4.30 per pack
Pair of Trousers	£12.55
Tie	£1.90
Sweatshirt	£8.75

Corey bought a pack of shirts, a tie and a pair of trousers.

How much change did he get from £20?

Show your working. You may get a mark.

£

2 marks

3. Match each of the fractions below to its equivalent decimal or percentage. One has been done for you.

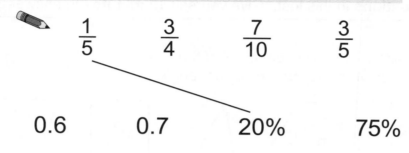

$$\frac{1}{5} \qquad \frac{3}{4} \qquad \frac{7}{10} \qquad \frac{3}{5}$$

0.6   0.7   20%   75%

_____
1 mark

4. Circle all of the numbers that are **greater** than 0.5.

0.52   0.9   0.4   0.36   0.07

_____
1 mark

5. A rectangular field has an area of 162 m².
The width of the field is 6 m.

What is the length of the field?

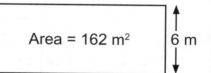

Area = 162 m²   6 m

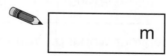

m

_____
1 mark

A different rectangular field also has an area of 162 m².
The width of this field is 9 m.

What is the **perimeter** of this field?

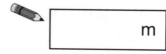

m

_____
1 mark

6. Invitations are sold in packs of 3.
Emily needs 77 invitations for her party.

How many packs of invitations does she need to buy?

packs

1 mark

7. This pie chart shows the costumes
worn by Year 3 at Halloween.

There are 72 children in Year 3.

How many children wore a zombie costume?

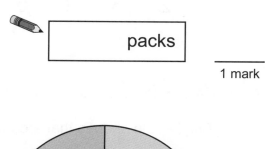

1 mark

11 children were dressed as a ghost.

How many were dressed as Dracula?

1 mark

END OF TEST

/ 10

Set A: Test 2

There are **7 questions** in this test. Give yourself **10 minutes** to answer them all.

1. Circle **all** the numbers below that are factors of 16.

   2   3   4   5   6   7   8   9

   _____
   1 mark

2. Each of the shapes below is divided into equal parts.

   Tick (✓) the shapes that are exactly $\frac{1}{3}$ shaded.

A	B	C	D	E

      ☐   ☐   ☐   ☐   ☐

   _____
   1 mark

3. Circle the appropriate measurements.

   a) The height of a car is approximately...

    13 cm   13 m   1.3 m   1.3 km   130 mm

   b) The mass of a mobile phone is approximately...

    120 g   12 kg   1.2 kg   12 g   120 kg

   c) A teaspoon holds approximately...

    5 litres   50 ml   50 litres   500 ml   5 ml

   _____
   1 mark

4. Emily counts the different vehicles that drive past her school one lunchtime. She records her results in a tally chart.

Vehicle	Tally
Car	ЖЖ ЖЖ
Van	ЖЖ III
Lorry	ЖЖ II
Motorbike	III

Use the information in the tally chart to complete this bar chart.

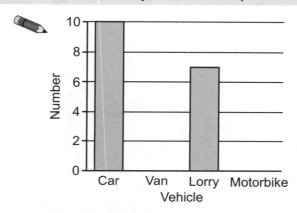

_____
1 mark

How many vehicles does Emily see altogether?

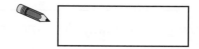

_____
1 mark

5. A model aeroplane costs £3.40. James gets a special deal. When he buys two aeroplanes, he saves 20% of the total price.

How much does he save altogether?

Show your working. You may get a mark.

£

_____
2 marks

6.   Look at the angles below.

   Circle any **obtuse** angles.

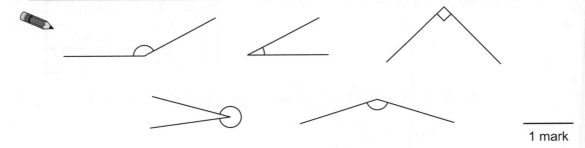

_____
1 mark

7.   A shop sells pet food.

   Corey buys $\frac{1}{2}$ kg of rabbit food
   and 3 tins of dog food.

£1.12 per kg

78p each

   How much does he spend in total?

Show your working. You may get a mark.

£

_____
2 marks

END OF TEST

/ 10

There are **7 questions** in this test. Give yourself **10 minutes** to answer them all.

1. Corey bought a 500 ml bottle of water.
    Here is the bottle after Corey had drunk some water.

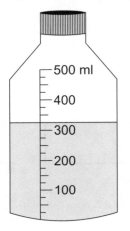

How much water did he drink?

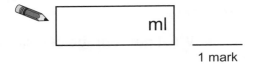

ml

---
1 mark

2. Here is part of a number wall.
    The shaded numbers are
    part of a sequence.

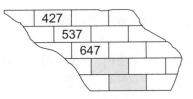

    Here is another part of the wall.
    The bricks are numbered
    using the same sequence.

What numbers belong on the two shaded bricks above?

and

---
2 marks

3.   Year 5 carried out a survey to find out what flavour
      jam they preferred. Here is a pictogram of their results.

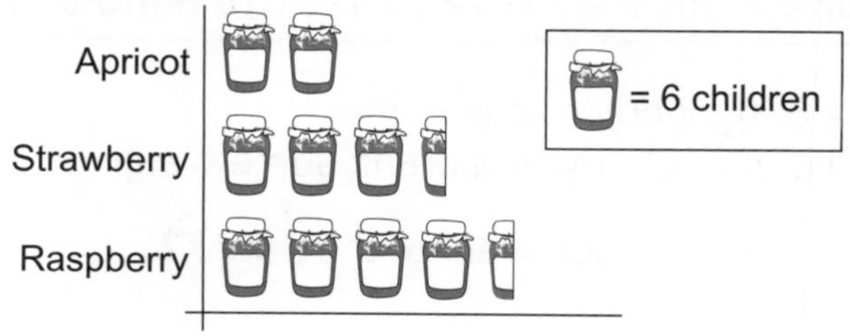

Apricot

Strawberry

Raspberry

= 6 children

How many more children chose strawberry than apricot?

1 mark

What **percentage** of children chose apricot?

%

1 mark

4.   Emily needs 60 g of fruit and 100 ml of juice to make a small smoothie.
      She follows the same recipe to make a large smoothie.
      A large smoothie uses 350 ml of juice.

How much fruit will she need?

Show your working. You may get a mark.

g

2 marks

5.   Write these numbers in order starting with the **smallest**.

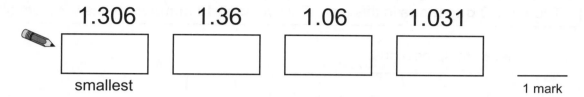

1.306   1.36   1.06   1.031

smallest   1 mark

6.   The diagram shows rectangle ABCD on a pair of axes.
     The lengths of its sides are 20 units and 5 units.

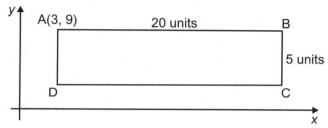

The coordinates of point A are (3, 9).

What are the coordinates of point C?

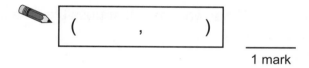

(,   )   ____

1 mark

7.   The temperature of a greenhouse was taken at regular intervals
     during the day. Here are the results.

     13°C   17°C   22°C   20°C   18°C

What was the mean temperature in the greenhouse that day?

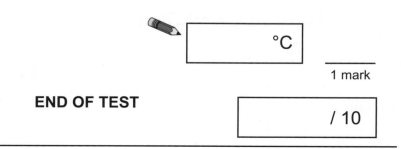

°C   ____

1 mark

END OF TEST

/ 10

13

There are **9 questions** in this test. Give yourself **10 minutes** to answer them all.

1. Here are some signs.

Use each sign once to make the calculation below correct.

7 ☐ 2 ☐ 9 ☐ 5

1 mark

2. Emily went to see a film at the local cinema.
It started at quarter past two in the afternoon.
It took her 25 minutes to walk from her house to the cinema.

What was the latest possible time she could leave her house?

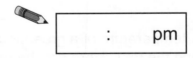

:   pm

1 mark

3. The outside temperature at midnight is –7°C.
By 11 am, the temperature has risen by 12°C.

What is the temperature at 11 am?

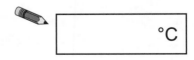

°C

1 mark

4.   Calculate 74.83 ÷ 7

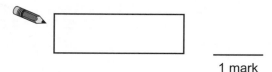

5.   Corey thinks of a number. He adds 25 to it then halves the result.
      Then he subtracts 17 and multiplies the result by 3.
      His final answer is 18.

      What number did Corey start with?

6.   Opposite faces of a dice add up to 7.

      Add spots to the blank faces of this net
      so that opposite faces add up to 7.

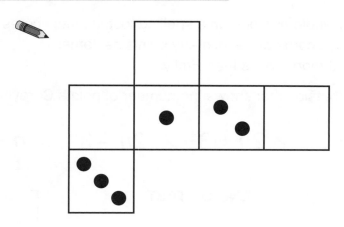

---

15   **Set A**: Test 5

7. A sign on Corey's house says it was built in MDCCCXXIX.

What year is this?

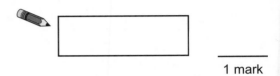

_____

8. Which of these cuboids has the greater volume?

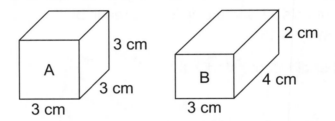

Show your working. You may get a mark.

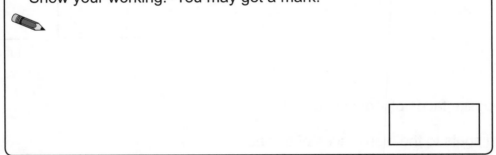

2 marks

9. n stands for a whole number. In a spelling test, James scores n points. Emily scores twice as many points as James. Corey scores 3 more points than Emily.

Circle the expression that shows the number of points Corey scored.

 $n^2 + 3$ $2n + 3$ $2n - 3$ $n + 3$ _____

1 mark

END OF TEST

/ 10

There are **8 questions** in this test. Give yourself **10 minutes** to answer them all. Show your working in the spaces and write your answers in the boxes.

1. $772 - 200$

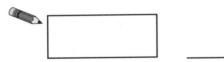

1 mark

2. $96 \div 6$

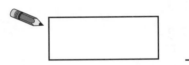

1 mark

3. $88 - 20 \times 4$

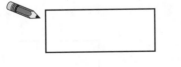

1 mark

4. $2\frac{3}{4} \times 8$

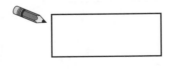

1 mark

5. 13.7 + 8.92

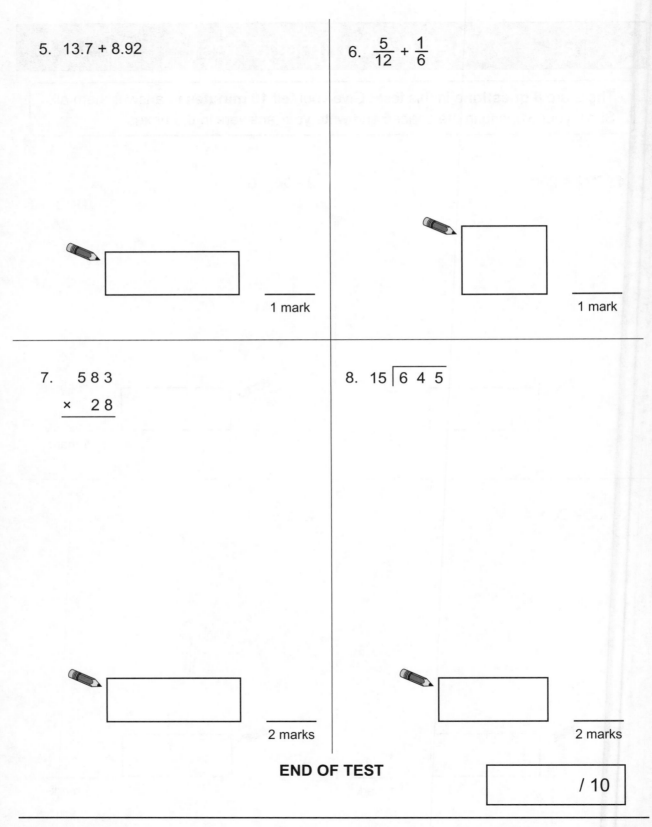

___

1 mark

6. $\frac{5}{12} + \frac{1}{6}$

___

1 mark

7.   5 8 3
    ×   2 8

___

2 marks

8. 15 ⟌ 6 4 5

___

2 marks

END OF TEST

/ 10

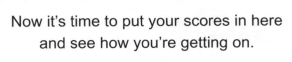

End of Set A: Scoresheet

You've finished a full set of tests — well done!

Now it's time to put your scores in here
and see how you're getting on.

	Score	
Test 1		/10
Test 2		/10
Test 3		/10
Test 4		/10
Test 5		/10
Arithmetic Test		/10
Total		**/60**

Once you've got a score out of 60, check it out in the table below...

0 – 29	If you got a lot of questions wrong, don't worry. **Practise** the topics you struggled with, then **have another go** at **this** set of tests.
30 – 45	If you got half-marks or better, you're doing well. Look back through the questions you got wrong and **brush up** on those topics. Then try the **next set** of tests.
46 – 60	Woohoo! Now have a go at the **next set** of tests — can you beat your score?

But before you do... bend your brain round this one:

Put four coins on a table, with the 'tails' side up. Turn any three coins over — that counts as a 'move'. In every move you must turn over <u>three different coins</u>. How many moves does it take to get all four coins facing 'heads' side up?

There are **8 questions** in this test. Give yourself **10 minutes** to answer them all.

1.   Shade in $\frac{1}{4}$ of this shape.

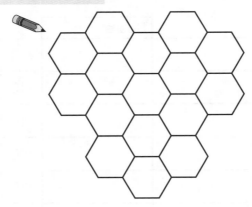

1 mark

2.   Here are three number cards.

$$\boxed{8} \quad \boxed{5} \quad \boxed{7}$$

Use each number once to make the following calculation correct.

$$\boxed{} \times \boxed{3} = \boxed{} + \boxed{}$$

1 mark

3.   Calculate 7.561 − 2.37

1 mark

4. The triangle on the right has a base of 8 m and a height of 10 m.

   Work out its area.

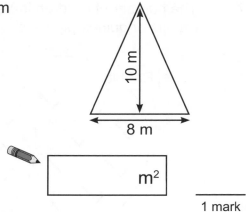

m²

5. Circle all the common factors of 24 and 40.

   1   2   3   4   6   8   10   12

6. Padma buys a bar of chocolate for £1.24 and two bags of sweets. The total cost is £3.68.

   How much does **one** bag of sweets cost?

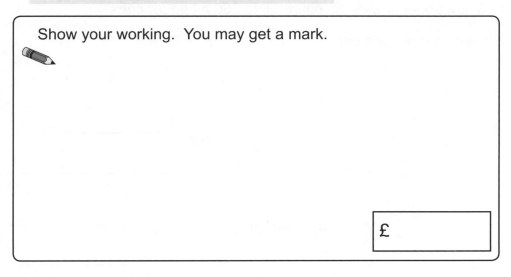

   Show your working. You may get a mark.

   £

7. The number of children in Year 5 who have rabbits or guinea pigs is shown below.

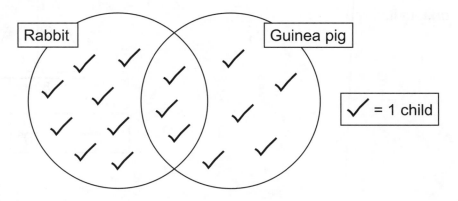

= 1 child

How many children in Year 5 only have a guinea pig?

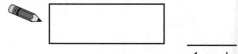

1 mark

How many children in Year 5 have a rabbit?

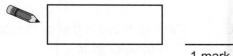

1 mark

8. A 1.75 litre bottle of water is poured into 250 ml paper cups.

How many paper cups can be filled?

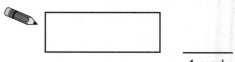

1 mark

END OF TEST

/ 10

There are **8 questions** in this test. Give yourself **10 minutes** to answer them all.

1.   Write in the two missing numbers in the sequence below.

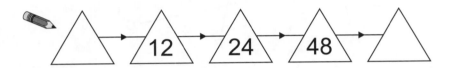

1 mark

2.   Draw the hour and minute hands on the clock face
     so that it shows the same time as the digital clock.

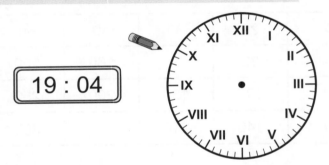

1 mark

3.   Write these fractions in order, starting with the **smallest**.

$$\frac{1}{2} \qquad \frac{3}{4} \qquad \frac{7}{12}$$

smallest

1 mark

---

4.   Josh draws 5 lines and labels them **A-E**.

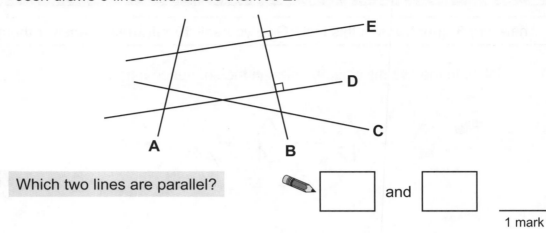

Which two lines are parallel?   ✏️ [   ] and [   ]

1 mark

5.   Fill in the three missing numbers in this multiplication grid.

✏️

×	20	30	40	50
4	80		160	200
	100	150	200	250
7	140	210		350

1 mark

6.   Padma cuts a roll of ribbon into 4.5 metre lengths.
      After cutting 6 lengths she has 75 cm left over.

      How long was the roll of ribbon she started with in **cm**?

      Show your working. You may get a mark.

      ✏️

      [   ] cm

2 marks

7.   This graph can be used to convert between inches and centimetres.

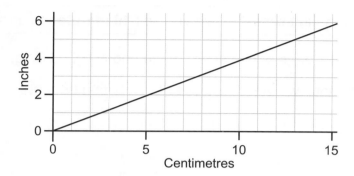

Use the graph to convert 4 inches into centimetres.
Give your answer to one decimal place.

| | cm |

8.   Kate has 5 cards. Y and Z stand for positive whole numbers.

When Kate adds up all the cards, she gets a total of 14.

Write down all the possible values of Y and Z.

END OF TEST

| / 10 |

There are **7 questions** in this test. Give yourself **10 minutes** to answer them all.

1. Padma bought 7 bags of bird seed. Each bag weighed 87 g.

   What was the total weight of bird seed that Padma bought?

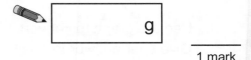

   g

   _____
   1 mark

2. Here are six number cards.

   7 8 2 4 9 5

   Use four of the cards to make the
   smallest possible **even** 4-digit number.

   _____
   1 mark

3. A bag contains 12 toffees. Kate eats 3 toffees and Josh eats 4 toffees.

   What fraction of the toffees are left?

   _____
   1 mark

4.   Use these shapes to complete the table of properties below.

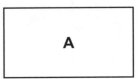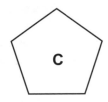

Shape	Name of Shape	Number of right angles	Lines of symmetry
A	rectangle		2
B	triangle	1	
C		0	5

1 mark

5.   Here is a tally chart showing the number of
library books not returned over a 4-month period.

Fill in the missing information to complete the tally chart.

Month	Number of books not returned	Total
April		13
May	‖‖‖ ‖‖‖ ‖‖‖ ‖‖‖ II	
June	‖‖‖ ‖‖‖ IIII	
July		11

1 mark

What is the **mean** number of books not returned per month?

1 mark

6. Without using a protractor, calculate the sizes of angles X and Y in this diagram.

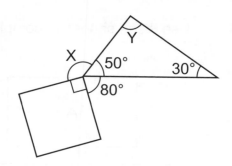

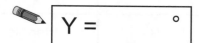

X = ____ °   Y = ____ °

_____
2 marks

7. Padma mixes 300 ml of her favourite drink. She uses 15% orange juice and 5% pineapple juice. The rest is lemonade.

How many ml of lemonade does she use?

Show your working. You may get a mark.

_____ ml

_____
2 marks

END OF TEST

/ 10

There are **7 questions** in this test. Give yourself **10 minutes** to answer them all.

1. Complete the following equivalent fractions.

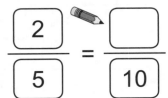 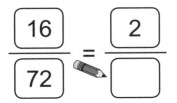

1 mark

2. Kate bought six chocolate cakes for £8.16.

How much does **one** cake cost?

£

1 mark

3. Here are some signs.

$>$ $<$ $=$

Use **two** of the signs to make these calculations correct.

9 × 6 ☐ 52

2 − 7 ☐ −3

1 mark

4. Josh has a kitten and a dog.
His kitten is shown on this scale.

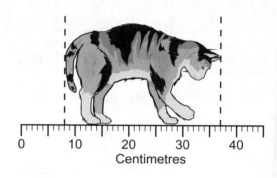

How long is his kitten?

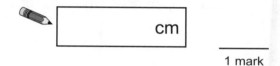 cm

1 mark

Together Josh's kitten and dog measure 1 m.

How long is his dog?

cm

1 mark

5. A circle has been drawn for you with its centre marked.

Draw a radius on the circle.

1 mark

A different circle has a radius of 17 mm.

What is its diameter?

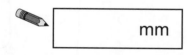 mm

1 mark

6. The following line graph shows Padma's height between the ages of 8 and 12.

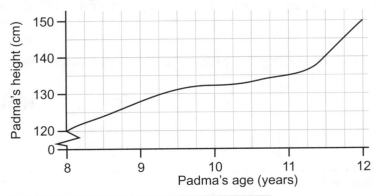

Padma's height (cm) / Padma's age (years)

How much did Padma grow between the ages of 11 and 12? Give your answer in metres.

m

7. A shop sells fish fingers in two boxes, A and B.
Box A contains 12 fish fingers and costs £2.52.
Box B contains 20 fish fingers and costs £3.80.

Which box is better value for money?

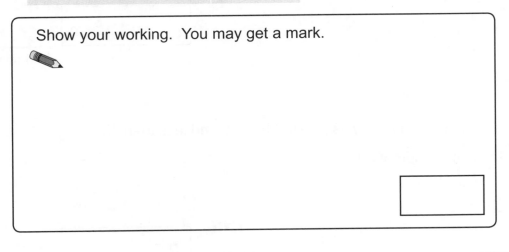

Show your working. You may get a mark.

END OF TEST

/ 10

There are **7 questions** in this test. Give yourself **10 minutes** to answer them all.

1. Write the following prices in order, starting with the **smallest**.

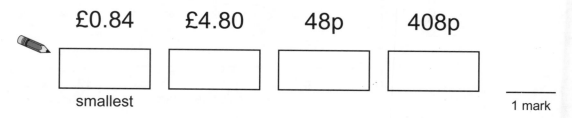

£0.84   £4.80   48p   408p

smallest

_____

1 mark

2. Kate's patio is made up of a rectangle and an isosceles triangle, as shown.

What is the **perimeter** of the patio?

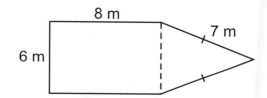

8 m

7 m

6 m

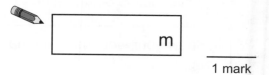

m

_____

1 mark

3. *p* is a whole number. 6*p* is greater than 40 and less than 45.

What is the value of *p*?

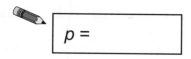

p =

_____

1 mark

4.   Convert the following measurements.

0.236 kilograms into grams.

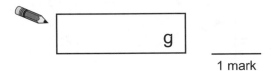

	g

1 mark

193 ounces into pounds and ounces.
1 lb = 16 oz

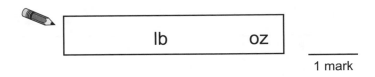

lb	oz

1 mark

5.   Padma cycles $3\frac{1}{4}$ miles. Josh cycles $\frac{7}{2}$ miles.

How far have they cycled in total? Give your answer as a mixed number.

Show your working. You may get a mark.

	miles

2 marks

6. Josh, Kate and Padma have been saving their pocket money.
Josh has saved £12. Kate has saved £3 less than Josh.
Padma has saved £2.50 more than Kate.

How much have they saved altogether?

Show your working. You may get a mark.

£

2 marks

7. The triangle ABC is translated
so that point A moves from (8, 14)
to (16, 10).
The new point is labelled A'.

What are the coordinates
of point B'?

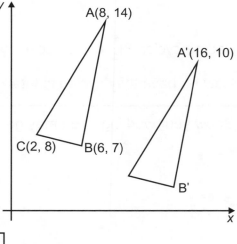

(,   )

1 mark

END OF TEST

/ 10

There are **8 questions** in this test. Give yourself **10 minutes** to answer them all. Show your working in the spaces and write your answers in the boxes.

1. 11 285 + 1000

2. $\frac{1}{5} \div 6$

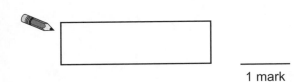

1 mark

1 mark

3. 2.1 × 5

4. 4 × 5 − 27 ÷ 3

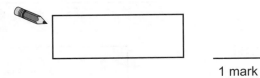

1 mark

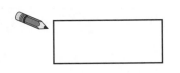

1 mark

5. $\frac{13}{12} - \frac{2}{3}$

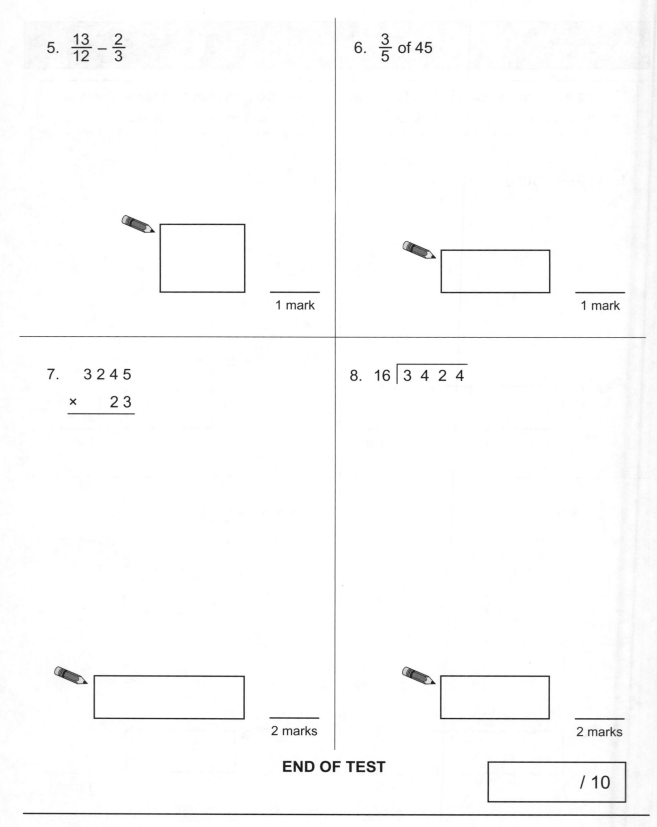

1 mark

6. $\frac{3}{5}$ of 45

1 mark

7.　　3 2 4 5
　　×　　2 3
　　———————

2 marks

8. 16 ⟌ 3 4 2 4

2 marks

END OF TEST

/ 10

End of Set B: Scoresheet

You've finished a full set of tests — well done!

Now it's time to put your scores in here
and see how you're getting on.

	Score	
Test 1		/10
Test 2		/10
Test 3		/10
Test 4		/10
Test 5		/10
Arithmetic Test		/10
Total		**/60**

Once you've got a score out of 60, check it out in the table below...

0 – 29	If you got a lot of questions wrong, don't worry. **Practise** the topics you struggled with, then **have another go** at **this** set of tests.
30 – 45	If you got half-marks or better, you're doing well. Look back through the questions you got wrong and **brush up** on those topics. Then try the **next set** of tests.
46 – 60	Woohoo! Now have a go at the **next set** of tests — can you beat your score?

But before you do... bend your brain round this one:

A farmer has 48 pieces of 1 metre long fencing. He wants to use all the fencing to make a rectangular or square pen to keep some of his animals in.

What is the largest possible area that he can make the animal pen?

There are **8 questions** in this test. Give yourself **10 minutes** to answer them all.

1.   Here are some number cards.

| 6 | 5 | 4 | 3 | 4 |

Write down the **smallest** and **largest** 3-digit
numbers that can be made using these cards.

Smallest ☐ ☐ ☐   Largest ☐ ☐ ☐

_____
1 mark

2.   Felix has 81 marbles. He divides them equally into 3 bags.

How many marbles are in each bag?

_____
1 mark

3.   Complete the table to show the equivalent
fractions, decimals and percentages.

Fraction	Decimal	Percentage
	0.63	 %
$\frac{23}{50}$		%

_____
2 marks

4. Anita has five **different** coins in her pocket.

What is the smallest total amount of money
that Anita could have in her pocket?

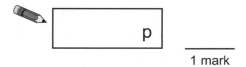

| | p |

5. Convert this mixed number to an improper fraction.

$$2\frac{1}{6} = \frac{\boxed{}}{\boxed{}}$$

6. A group of children were asked about their favourite type of film.
The results are shown in the table below.

	Boys	Girls
Action	19	18
Horror	31	14
Comedy	12	27
Romance	13	29

For which type of film was there the greatest
difference between boys and girls?

7.   Write in the missing numbers to make these calculations correct.

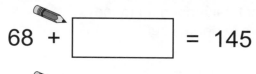

$$68 + \boxed{} = 145$$

$$11 \times \boxed{} = 132$$

___

1 mark

8.   Here is a bus timetable between Podton and Ferndale.

Podton	08:20	08:30	08:40	09:00	09:20
Lawford	08:35	08:45	—	09:15	09:35
Brambly	09:00	09:10	09:05	09:40	10:00
Hilland	—	09:25	—	—	—
Ferndale	09:32	09:55	09:37	10:12	10:32

How long does it take to get the bus from Podton to Hilland?

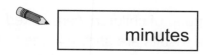

$$\boxed{} \text{ minutes}$$

___

1 mark

Anita catches the bus from Lawford. She arrives in Ferndale at 10:12.

What time did her bus leave Lawford?
Give your answer using the 12-hour clock.

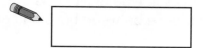

$$\boxed{}$$

___

1 mark

END OF TEST

$$\boxed{ / 10}$$

There are **7 questions** in this test. Give yourself **10 minutes** to answer them all.

1. This shape is made from identical tiles.

    Shade in more tiles so that exactly $\frac{1}{3}$ of the shape is shaded.

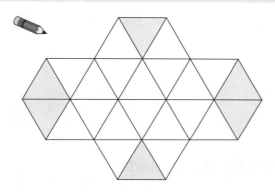

1 mark

2. Write the rounded numbers in the boxes below.

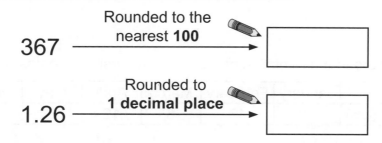

    367 — Rounded to the nearest **100** →

    1.26 — Rounded to **1 decimal place** →

1 mark

3. In these calculations, the missing sign is either =, < or >.

    Write in the missing sign to make each calculation correct.

    4 + 8 ☐ 3 + 6   6 − 3 ☐ 8 − 4

    3 × 6 ☐ 4 × 8   8 ÷ 4 ☐ 6 ÷ 3

2 marks

4.   A sketch of a triangle is shown to the right.

Use a ruler and protractor to draw the triangle accurately.

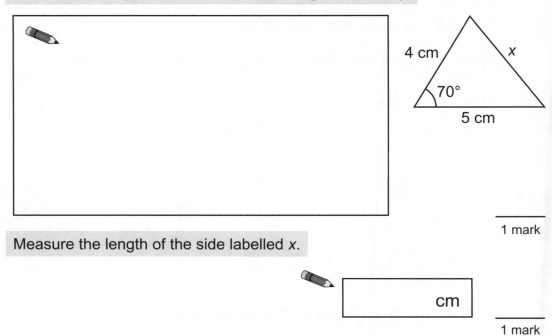

4 cm

x

70°

5 cm

1 mark

Measure the length of the side labelled *x*.

cm

1 mark

5.   Anita recorded the rainfall in her town for the first six months of last year.

Month	January	February	March	April	May	June
Rainfall (cm)	19	17	8	12	6	3

Complete the line graph below to show all the information from the table.

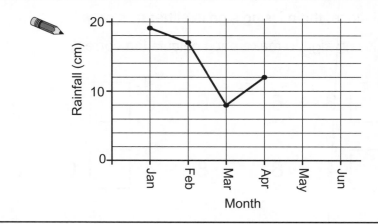

1 mark

6. Zac and Felix share some grapes in the ratio 4 : 5.
Zac gets 24 grapes.

How many grapes does Felix get?

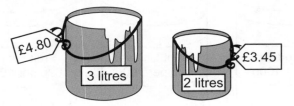

1 mark

7. Paint is sold in two different sized tins.

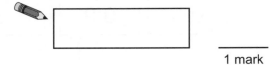

£4.80 3 litres £3.45 2 litres

Felix and Anita each buy 6 litres of paint.
Felix buys three 2-litre tins and Anita buys two 3-litre tins.

How much more does Felix pay than Anita?

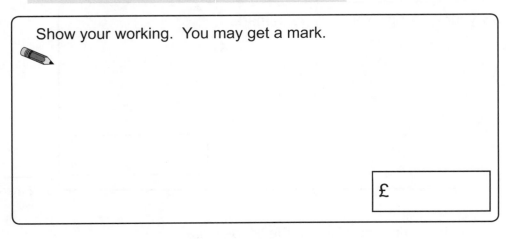

Show your working. You may get a mark.

£

2 marks

END OF TEST

/ 10

Set C: Test 3

There are **7 questions** in this test. Give yourself **10 minutes** to answer them all.

1. The sequence below increases by the same amount each time.

   Fill in the next two numbers in the sequence.

   | 0.5 | 0.9 | 1.3 | | | |

   _____

   1 mark

2. A shop sells sweets by weight.

   Jelly Teddies
   72p per 100g

   Mint Chews
   46p per 100g

   Fruit Drops
   62p per 100g

   Zac buys 50 g of Mint Chews and 300 g of Jelly Teddies.

   How much did he spend altogether?

   Show your working. You may get a mark.

   £ _____

   _____

   2 marks

3. Circle the **two** prime numbers in the list below.

      8   13   27   39   41   55

   _____

   1 mark

---

4. Here is part of a number line.

Write down the number shown by the arrow.

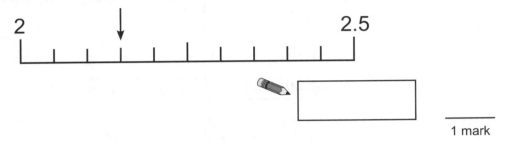

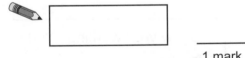

_____
1 mark

5. This chart shows the sports equipment sold by a shop last week.

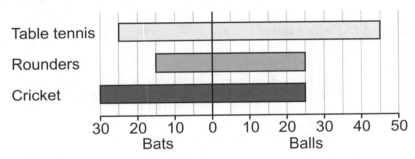

How many **more** cricket bats were sold than cricket balls?

_____
1 mark

Zac says, "More than half of the total items sold were for table tennis."

Is Zac correct? Show how you know.

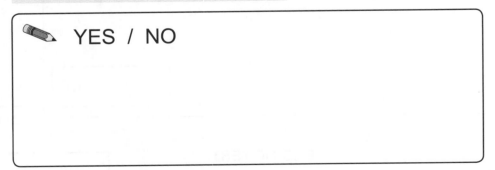

YES / NO

_____
1 mark

6. Reflect shape A in the *y*-axis.

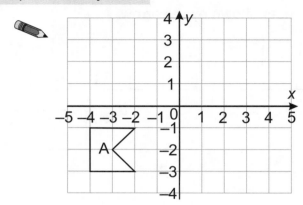

7. Here is a plan of Felix's lawn.

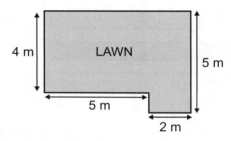

4 m LAWN 5 m

5 m

2 m

What is the area of the lawn?

Show your working. You may get a mark.

m²

END OF TEST

/ 10

There are **7 questions** in this test. Give yourself **10 minutes** to answer them all.

1. What is the difference between the
   temperatures in Paris and New York?

Paris: New York:
4°C   −5°C

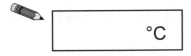

°C

_____
1 mark

2. Felix had £2.50. He spent half of his money on a comic,
   then bought a bar of chocolate for 72p.

   How much money does he have left?

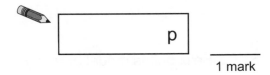

p

_____
1 mark

3. Use a protractor to find the size of angle *y*.

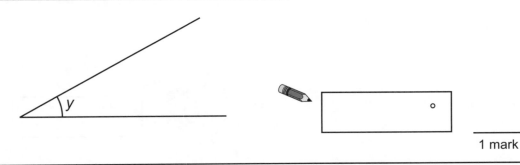

y

°

_____
1 mark

4. Look at the shape on the right.

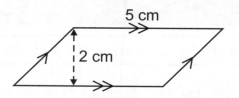

5 cm

2 cm

For each statement, put a tick (✓) in the box if the statement is true or a cross (✗) if the statement is false.

Its opposite angles are equal.

It is called a parallelogram.

It has four lines of symmetry.

Find the area of the shape above.

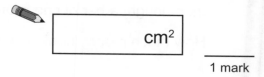

cm²

5. Felix builds model aeroplanes. He uses 6 tubes of glue for every 8 models that he builds. Last month he built 20 model aeroplanes.

How many tubes of glue did he use?

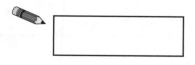

6. Zac walks 1560 m to the park, then walks another 2440 m to the beach.

How far has he walked in total?

Give your answer in km.

$\boxed{ \text{km}}$

Approximately how far is this in miles?

5 miles ≈ 8 km

$\boxed{ \text{miles}}$

7. A shop stocks 30 bottles of shampoo. Felix buys $\frac{2}{5}$ of the bottles and Anita buys $\frac{3}{10}$ of the bottles.

How many bottles of shampoo does the shop have left?

Show your working. You may get a mark.

$\boxed{}$

END OF TEST

$\boxed{ / 10}$

There are **8 questions** in this test. Give yourself **10 minutes** to answer them all.

1. Put a ring around the number that is closest to 750.

     736   766

    _____
    1 mark

2. Which **two** of the shapes below have exactly 5 faces?

    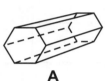 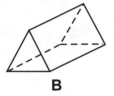

    A   **B**   **C**   **D**   **E**

     [   ] and [   ]

    _____
    1 mark

3. Find **two** common multiples of 8 and 12 between 1 and 50.

    [   ] and [   ]

    _____
    1 mark

4. A ring is valued at £280. Felix buys it at 75% of its value.

    How much did Felix pay for the ring?

     £ [   ]

    _____
    1 mark

5.   A school needs 4500 paperclips, which are sold in boxes of 200.

How many boxes must the school buy?

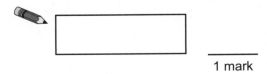

1 mark

A box of paperclips costs £2.70.

What is the price of 8 boxes of paperclips?

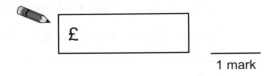

£

1 mark

6.   Enlarge shape B by a scale factor of 3.

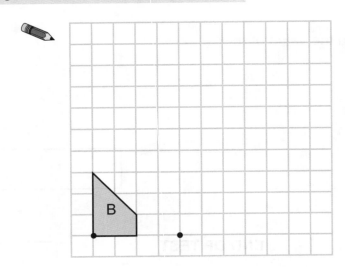

1 mark

7. This bar chart shows how long
    it takes the children in Year 6
    to walk to school each morning.

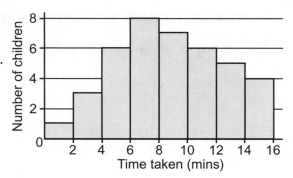

How many children take longer than
10 minutes to walk to school?

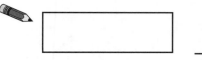

1 mark

Zac says, "4 children take between 6 and 7 minutes to walk to school."

Explain why he cannot work this out from the graph.

1 mark

8. When $n = 6$, find the value of $n^2 + 3n$.

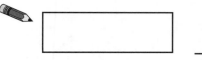

1 mark

END OF TEST

/ 10

There are **8 questions** in this test. Give yourself **10 minutes** to answer them all. Show your working in the spaces and write your answers in the boxes.

---

1. 5943 + 100

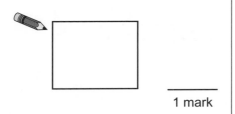

1 mark

2. 15.8 − 12

1 mark

---

3. 2³

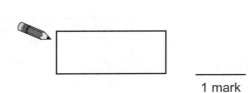

1 mark

4. 38.4 ÷ 16

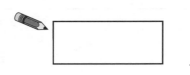

1 mark

---

5. 15% of 640

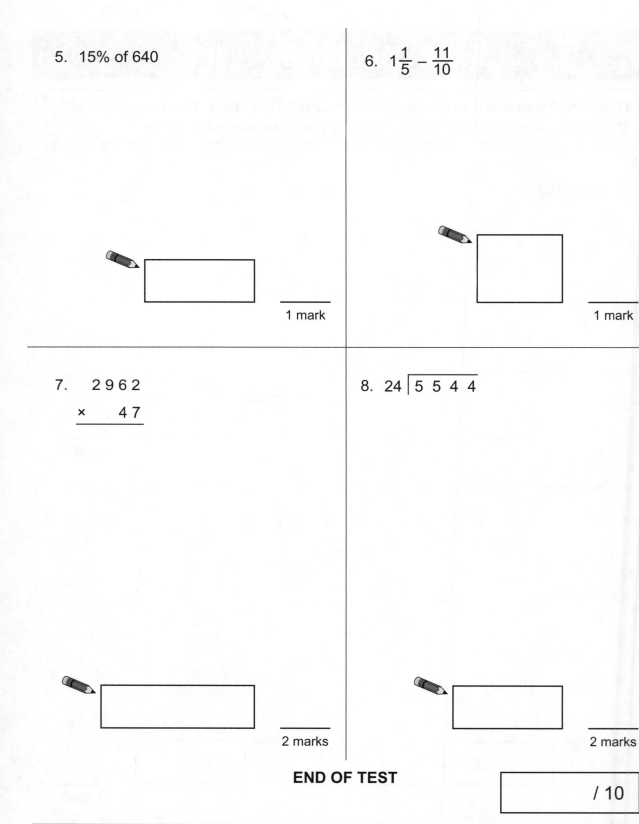

1 mark

6. $1\frac{1}{5} - \frac{11}{10}$

1 mark

7. $\begin{array}{r} 2\,9\,6\,2 \\ \times \quad 4\,7 \\ \hline \end{array}$

2 marks

8. $24\,\overline{\smash{\big)}\,5\,5\,4\,4}$

2 marks

END OF TEST

/ 10

54

End of Set C: Scoresheet

You've finished a full set of tests — well done!

Now it's time to put your scores in here
and see how you're getting on.

	Score	
Test 1		/10
Test 2		/10
Test 3		/10
Test 4		/10
Test 5		/10
Arithmetic Test		/10
Total		**/60**

Once you've got a score out of 60, check it out in the table below...

0 – 29	If you got a lot of questions wrong, don't worry. **Practise** the topics you struggled with, then **have another go** at **this** set of tests.
30 – 45	If you got half-marks or better, you're doing well. Look back through the questions you got wrong and **brush up** on those topics until you're happy with them.
46 – 60	Woohoo! You've done really well — congratulations.

One last thing... bend your brain round this one:

Draw out a 3×3 square like the one shown in this diagram.
Can you put the digits 1-9 into the square so that the digits in
each row, each column and the two diagonals add up to 15?

Answers

Set A

Test 1 — pages 2-4

1. **1 mark for both digits correct**

   24 + 76 = 100
   Topic tested: ADDITION

2. **1 mark**

   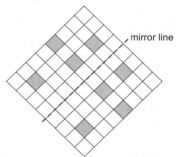

   mirror line

   Topic tested: SYMMETRY

3. **1 mark for both correct**

   900 × 4 = 3600
   560 ÷ 8 = 70
   Topics tested: MULTIPLICATION &
   DIVISION

4. **1 mark**

   2.4 kg
   Topic tested: READING SCALES

5. **1 mark for correct answer**

   8 + 17 + 16 = 41
   Topics tested: TABLES & ADDITION

6. **1 mark for all three correct**

   4.05 to the nearest whole number is 4
   8.52 to the nearest whole number is 9
   16.79 to the nearest whole number is 17
   Topic tested: ROUNDING

7. **1 mark**

   48
   Topic tested: SQUARE NUMBERS

8. **1 mark for both correct answers**

   English and Science
   Topic tested: BAR CHARTS

9. **2 marks for the correct answer,**
   otherwise 1 mark for correct working

   There are 4 × 7 = 28 days in 4 weeks, so the
   duck swims 4 × 28 = 112 lengths in 4 weeks.

   $$\begin{array}{r} 1\,1\,2 \\ \times\quad 3\,6 \\ \hline 6\,7{,}2 \\ 3\,3\,6\,0 \\ \hline 4\,0\,3\,2\,m \\ \hline \end{array}$$

   Topic tested: MULTIPLICATION

Test 2 — pages 5-7

1. **1 mark for all three correct**

   A, B and D
   Topics tested: ANGLES & SHAPES

2. **2 marks for correct answer**
   otherwise 1 mark for correct working

   Corey spent:
   $$\begin{array}{r} 4\,.\,3\,0 \\ 1\,.\,9\,0 \\ +\,1\,2\,.\,5\,5 \\ \hline £\,1\,8\,.\,7\,5 \\ \hline \end{array}$$

   Corey's change: £20 − £18.75 = £1.25
   Topic tested: CALCULATIONS WITH
   MONEY

3. **1 mark for all lines correct**

   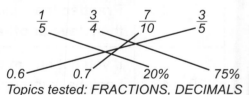

   Topics tested: FRACTIONS, DECIMALS
   & PERCENTAGES

4. **1 mark for both correct**

   0.52 and 0.9
   Topic tested: ORDERING DECIMALS

5. **1 mark for correct answer**

   $$6\overline{)1\,6\,{}^{4}2}\ \ ^{2\,7\,m}$$

   1 mark for correct answer

   $$9\overline{)1\,6\,{}^{7}2}\ \ ^{1\,8\,m}$$

   18 + 9 + 18 + 9 = 54 m
   Topics tested: AREA & PERIMETER

Answers

6. 1 mark for correct answer

$$3\overline{)7\,^17}\quad \begin{array}{c}2\;5\;r\,2\end{array}$$

So she needs to buy 26 packs.
Topic tested: DIVISION

7. 1 mark for correct answer

Zombie section makes up $\frac{1}{4}$ of the circle:
$\frac{1}{4}$ of 72 = $4\overline{)7\,^32}\quad \begin{array}{c}1\;8\end{array}$

1 mark for correct answer

Ghost and Dracula sections make up half
of the circle:
72 ÷ 2 = 36
36 – 11 = 25
Topics tested: PIE CHARTS & ANGLES

Test 3 — pages 8-10

1. 1 mark for all three correct
2, 4 and 8
Topic tested: FACTORS

2. 1 mark for both correct
B and D
Topic tested: FRACTIONS

3. 1 mark for all three correct

a) *1.3 m*

b) *120 g*

c) *5 ml*
Topics tested: UNITS & MEASURES

4. 1 mark for both bars correct

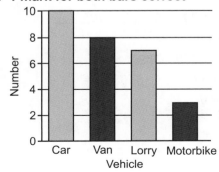

1 mark for correct answer

10 + 8 + 7 + 3 = 28
Topics tested: BAR CHARTS & TABLES

5. 2 marks for correct answer
otherwise 1 mark for correct working

£3.40 × 2 = £6.80
10% of £6.80 = £6.80 ÷ 10 = 68p
20% of £6.80 = 68p × 2 = £1.36
Topic tested: PERCENTAGES

6. 1 mark for both correct angles circled

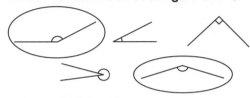

Topic tested: ANGLES

7. 2 marks for correct answer
otherwise 1 mark for correct working

£1.12 ÷ 2 = 56p
78p × 3 = £2.34
56p + £2.34 = £2.90
Topic tested: CALCULATIONS WITH MONEY

Test 4 — pages 11-13

1. 1 mark for correct answer

There are 325 ml of water left
500 – 325 = 175 ml
Topic tested: READING SCALES

2. 1 mark for each correct answer

The sequence rule is add 110 each time.

757 and 867
Topic tested: SEQUENCES

3. 1 mark for correct answer

Half a jar represents 6 ÷ 2 = 3 children
6 × 2 = 12 children chose apricot
(6 × 3) + 3 = 21 children chose strawberry
21 – 12 = 9 more children chose
strawberry than apricot.

Answers

1 mark for correct answer

There are 10 jars in total, and 2 are apricot.

$\frac{2}{10} = \frac{1}{5} = 20\%$

Topics tested: PICTOGRAMS & PERCENTAGES

4. **2 marks for correct answer otherwise 1 mark for correct working**

If 100 ml needs 60 g fruit then 300 ml needs 60 × 3 = 180 g fruit and 50 ml needs 60 ÷ 2 = 30 g fruit. Total fruit needed for 350 ml is 180 g + 30 g = 210 g

Topics tested: RATIO & PROPORTION

5. **1 mark for correct order**

1.031, 1.06, 1.306, 1.36

Topic tested: ORDERING DECIMALS

6. **1 mark for correct answer**

3 + 20 = 23
9 − 5 = 4
(23, 4)

Topic tested: COORDINATES

7. **1 mark for correct answer**

13 + 17 + 22 + 20 + 18 = 90
90 ÷ 5 = 18°C

Topic tested: MEAN

Test 5 — pages 14-16

1. **1 mark for all three signs correct**

7 × 2 = 9 + 5

Topic tested: ORDER OF OPERATIONS

2. **1 mark**

1:50 pm

Topic tested: TIME

3. **1 mark for correct answer**

−7 + 12 = 5°C

Topic tested: NEGATIVE NUMBERS

4. **1 mark for correct answer**

$\begin{array}{r} 10.\ 6\ 9 \\ 7\overline{)74.^48^63} \end{array}$

Topic tested: DIVIDING DECIMALS

5. **1 mark for correct answer**

18 ÷ 3 = 6
6 + 17 = 23
23 × 2 = 46
46 − 25 = 21

Topic tested: INVERSE OPERATIONS

6. **1 mark for all three faces correct**

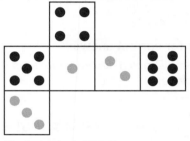

Topic tested: NETS

7. **1 mark for the correct answer**

MDCCCXXIX = 1000 + 500 + 300 + 20 + 9
= 1829

Topic tested: ROMAN NUMERALS

8. **2 marks for correct answer otherwise 1 mark for correct working**

Volume of cuboid A = 3 × 3 × 3 = 27 cm³
Volume of cuboid B = 3 × 4 × 2 = 24 cm³
So cuboid A has the greater volume

Topic tested: VOLUME

9. **1 mark**

2n + 3

Topic tested: ALGEBRA

Arithmetic Test — pages 17-18

1. **1 mark**

772 − 200 = 572

2. **1 mark**

$\begin{array}{r} 1\ 6 \\ 6\overline{)9\ ^36} \end{array}$

3. **1 mark**

88 − 20 × 4 = 88 − 80 = 8

Answers

4. 1 mark

$2 \times 8 = 16$

$\frac{3}{4} \times 8 = 6$

$16 + 6 = 22$

5. 1 mark

```
  1 3 . 7 0
+    8 . 9 2
  2 2 . 6 2
     1 1
```

6. 1 mark

$\frac{5}{12} + \frac{1}{6} = \frac{5}{12} + \frac{2}{12} = \frac{7}{12}$

7. 2 marks for correct answer otherwise 1 mark for correct working

```
      5 8 3
×       2 8
    4 6₆6₂4
  1 1₁6 6 0
  1 6 3 2 4
     1 1
```

8. 2 marks for correct answer otherwise 1 mark for correct working

```
        4 3
  15 ) 6 4 5
     − 6 0
        4 5
     − 4 5
          0
```

Scoresheet Question — page 19

A minimum of 4 moves.
E.g. TTTT, THHH, HTTH, HHHT, TTTT

Set B

Test 1 — pages 20-22

1. 1 mark for exactly 4 shaded hexagons

E.g.

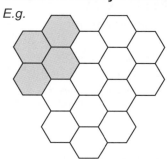

Topic tested: FRACTIONS

2. 1 mark for a correct answer

$5 \times 3 = 7 + 8$ or $5 \times 3 = 8 + 7$
Topic tested: NUMBER PROBLEMS

3. 1 mark for correct answer

```
    4 1
  7 . 5̷ 6̷ 1
− 2 . 3 7 0
  5 . 1 9 1
```

Topic tested: SUBTRACTING DECIMALS

4. 1 mark

Area $= \frac{1}{2} \times$ base $\times$ height

$= \frac{1}{2} \times 8 \times 10 = 40 \ m^2$

Topic tested: AREA

5. 1 mark for all 4 circled

Factors of 24: 1, 2, 3, 4, 6, 8, 12, 24
Factors of 40: 1, 2, 4, 5, 8, 10, 20, 40
So 1, 2, 4 and 8 should be circled
Topic tested: FACTORS

6. 2 marks for correct answer otherwise 1 mark for the correct cost of two bags of sweets

```
  3 . 6 8
− 1 . 2 4
£ 2 . 4 4
```
for two bags of sweets

£2.44 ÷ 2 = £1.22 for one bag of sweets
Topic tested: CALCULATIONS WITH MONEY

Answers

7. 1 mark

5

1 mark

11

Topic tested: DIAGRAMS

8. 1 mark for correct answer

1.75 l = 1750 ml
250 ml × 4 = 1000 ml
250 ml × 3 = 750 ml
So 4 + 3 = 7 cups can be filled
Topics tested: CONVERTING UNITS &
DIVISION

Test 2 — pages 23-25

1. 1 mark for both correct

The rule is 'multiply the previous term by 2'
6 and 96
Topic tested: SEQUENCES

2. 1 mark for correct answer

Topic tested: TIME

3. 1 mark for correct order

Change each fraction into twelfths:
$$\frac{1}{2} = \frac{6}{12}, \ \frac{3}{4} = \frac{9}{12}, \ \frac{7}{12}$$

So in order, they are:
$$\frac{1}{2}, \ \frac{7}{12}, \ \frac{3}{4}$$
Topic tested: ORDERING FRACTIONS

4. 1 mark for both correct

D and E
Topic tested: PARALLEL LINES

5. 1 mark for all three correct

×	20	30	40	50
4	80	**120**	160	200
5	100	150	200	250
7	140	210	**280**	350

Topic tested: MULTIPLICATION

6. 2 marks for correct answer
otherwise 1 mark for correct working

4.5 m × 6 = 27 m
27 × 100 = 2700 cm
2700 + 75 = 2775 cm
Topics tested: NUMBER PROBLEMS &
CONVERTING UNITS

7. 1 mark for a correct answer

10.1, 10.2 or 10.3
Topic tested: LINE GRAPHS

8. 2 marks for all three correct pairs,
otherwise 1 mark for two correct pairs

4Y + Z = 14
Possible values are:
Y = 1, Z = 10
Y = 2, Z = 6
Y = 3, Z = 2
Topic tested: MISSING NUMBERS

Test 3 — pages 26-28

1. 1 mark for correct answer

```
    8 7
 ×    7
  6 0 9 g
    4
```

Topic tested: MULTIPLICATION

2. 1 mark

2458
Topic tested: NUMBER PROBLEMS

3. 1 mark for correct answer

12 – 3 – 4 = 5 toffees left
$$\frac{5}{12} \ are \ left$$
Topic tested: FRACTIONS

Answers

4. 1 mark for all three correct

Shape	Name of Shape	Number of right angles	Lines of symmetry
A	rectangle	4	2
B	triangle	1	0
C	pentagon	0	5

Topics tested: SHAPES & SYMMETRY

5. 1 mark for table filled in correctly

Month	Number of books not returned	Total
April	‖‖‖ ‖‖‖ |||	13
May	‖‖‖ ‖‖‖ ‖‖‖ ‖‖‖ ||	22
June	‖‖‖ ‖‖‖ ||||	14
July	‖‖‖ ‖‖‖		11

1 mark for correct answer
13 + 22 + 14 + 11 = 60
60 ÷ 4 = 15 books
Topics tested: TALLY CHARTS & MEAN

6. 1 mark for each correct angle
$X + 50° + 80° + 90° = 360°$
$X = 360° − 220° = 140°$
$Y + 50° + 30° = 180°$
$Y = 180° − 80° = 100°$
Topic tested: ANGLES

7. 2 marks for correct answer otherwise 1 mark for correct working
100% − 15% − 5% = 80%
10% of 300 ml = 300 ml ÷ 10 = 30 ml
80% of 300 ml = 30 ml × 8 = 240 ml
Topic tested: PERCENTAGES

Test 4 — pages 29-31

1. 1 mark for both correct answers
$\frac{2}{5} = \frac{4}{10}$ and $\frac{16}{72} = \frac{2}{9}$
Topic tested: FRACTIONS

2. 1 mark for correct answer
$$6)\overline{8.^2 1^3 6} = £1.36$$
Topic tested: DIVISION

3. 1 mark for both signs correct
$9 × 6 > 52$
$2 − 7 < −3$
Topics tested: COMPARING NUMBERS & NEGATIVE NUMBERS

4. 1 mark for correct answer
37 − 8 = 29 cm

1 mark for correct answer
100 − 29 = 71 cm
Topics tested: READING SCALES & SUBTRACTION

5. 1 mark for a correct radius
E.g.

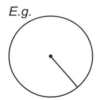

1 mark
Diameter = 2 × radius = 2 × 17 = 34 mm
Topic tested: CIRCLES

6. 1 mark for correct answer
Height at age 11 = 135 cm
Height at age 12 = 150 cm
150 − 135 = 15 cm = 0.15 m
Topics tested: LINE GRAPHS & CONVERTING UNITS

7. 1 mark for correct answer
1 mark for correct working
Box A:
£2.52 ÷ 12 = £0.21 = 21p per fish finger
Box B:
£3.80 ÷ 20 = £0.19 = 19p per fish finger
So box B is better value for money.
Topic tested: CALCULATIONS WITH MONEY

Answers

Test 5 — pages 32-34

1. **1 mark for all four values in the correct order**

   48p, £0.84, 408p, £4.80
   Topic tested: PLACE VALUE

2. **1 mark for correct answer**

   The triangle is isosceles, so the missing side of the triangle is 7 m. The missing side of the rectangle is 8 m.
   Perimeter = 8 + 7 + 7 + 8 + 6 = 36 m
   Topic tested: PERIMETER

3. **1 mark for correct answer**

   Multiples of 6 are ..., 36, 42, 48, ...
   42 is the only one between 40 and 45,
   so 6p = 42 which means p = 7.
   Topic tested: ALGEBRA

4. **1 mark for correct answer**

   0.236 × 1000 = 236 g

   1 mark for correct answer

   $$16\overline{)19\,^3 3}\quad\frac{1\;2\;r\,1}{}$$

   So 193 ounces = 12 lb 1 oz
   Topic tested: UNIT CONVERSIONS

5. **2 marks for the correct answer otherwise 1 mark for correct working**

   $$3\frac{1}{4} + \frac{7}{2} = \frac{13}{4} + \frac{7}{2} = \frac{13}{4} + \frac{14}{4} = \frac{27}{4}$$
   $$= 6\frac{3}{4}\ miles$$

   Topics tested: ADDING FRACTIONS & MIXED NUMBERS

6. **2 marks for correct answer otherwise 1 mark for correct working**

   Josh = £12
   Kate = £12 − £3 = £9
   Padma = £9 + £2.50 = £11.50
   Total = £12 + £9 + £11.50 = £32.50
   Topic tested: CALCULATIONS WITH MONEY

7. **1 mark for both coordinates correct**

   To get from (8, 14) to (16, 10), add 8 to the x-coordinate and subtract 4 from the y-coordinate.
   So B(6, 7) becomes
   B'(6 + 8, 7 − 4) = (14, 3)
   Topics tested: TRANSLATION & COORDINATES

Arithmetic Test — pages 35-36

1. **1 mark**

   11 285 + 1000 = 12 285

2. **1 mark**

   $$\frac{1}{5} \div 6 = \frac{1}{5 \times 6} = \frac{1}{30}$$

3. **1 mark**

   $$2.1 \times 5 = 2 \times 5 + 0.1 \times 5$$
   $$= 10 + 0.5$$
   $$= 10.5$$

4. **1 mark**

   $$4 \times 5 - 27 \div 3 = 20 - 9 = 11$$

5. **1 mark**

   $$\frac{13}{12} - \frac{2}{3} = \frac{13}{12} - \frac{8}{12} = \frac{5}{12}$$

6. **1 mark**

   $$\frac{1}{5}\ of\ 45 = 45 \div 5 = 9$$
   $$\frac{3}{5}\ of\ 45 = 9 \times 3 = 27$$

7. **2 marks for correct answer otherwise 1 mark for correct working**

   $$\begin{array}{r}
   3\,2\,4\,5 \\
   \times\quad 2\,3 \\
   \hline
   9\,7_{,1}3_{,1}5 \\
   6\,4\,9_{,1}0\,0 \\
   \hline
   7\,4\,6\,3\,5 \\
   \hline
   {\scriptstyle 1\ \ 1}
   \end{array}$$

Answers

8. **2 marks for correct answer**
otherwise 1 mark for correct working

$$16 \overline{)\,3\,4\,2\,4\,}$$
$$2\,1\,4$$
$$-3\,2$$
$$2\,2$$
$$-1\,6$$
$$6\,4$$
$$-6\,4$$
$$0$$

Scoresheet Question — page 37

Largest area = 12 m × 12 m = 144 m²
(Square pen with sides of length 12 m.)

Set C

Test 1 — pages 38-40

1. **1 mark for both correct**

Smallest: 344
Largest: 654
Topic tested: NUMBER PROBLEMS

2. **1 mark for correct answer**

$$3 \overline{)\,8\,^21\,}$$
$$2\,7$$

Topic tested: DIVISION

3. **2 marks for both rows filled in correctly,**
otherwise 1 mark for one row filled in
correctly

Fraction	Decimal	Percentage
$\frac{63}{100}$	0.63	63%
$\frac{23}{50}$	0.46	46%

Topics tested: FRACTIONS, DECIMALS
& PERCENTAGES

4. **1 mark for correct answer**

1p + 2p + 5p + 10p + 20p = 38p
Topic tested: CALCULATIONS WITH
MONEY

5. **1 mark for correct answer**

$2 = \frac{12}{6}$, so $2\frac{1}{6} = \frac{12}{6} + \frac{1}{6} = \frac{13}{6}$

Topic tested: FRACTIONS

6. **1 mark for correct answer**

Action: 19 − 18 = 1
Horror: 31 − 14 = 17
Comedy: 27 − 12 = 15
Romance: 29 − 13 = 16
The biggest difference is in horror films.
Topics tested: TABLES & SUBTRACTION

7. **1 mark for both correct**

68 + 77 = 145
11 × 12 = 132
Topics tested: ADDITION &
MULTIPLICATION

8. **1 mark for correct answer**

08:30 to 09:00 = 30 minutes
09:00 to 09:25 = 25 minutes
30 + 25 = 55 minutes

1 mark for correct answer

09:15 = 9.15 am
Topic tested: TIMETABLES

Test 2 — pages 41-43

1. **1 mark for shading any two extra triangles**
E.g.

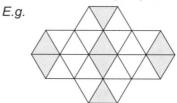

Topic tested: FRACTIONS

2. **1 mark for both correct**

367 rounded to the nearest 100 is 400
1.26 rounded to 1 decimal place is 1.3
Topic tested: ROUNDING

3. **2 marks for all four signs correct**
otherwise 1 mark for two signs correct

4 + 8 > 3 + 6   6 − 3 < 8 − 4
3 × 6 < 4 × 8   8 ÷ 4 = 6 ÷ 3
Topic tested: COMPARING NUMBERS

4. **1 mark for triangle drawn accurately**

1 mark for a correct answer

5.1 cm, 5.2 cm or 5.3 cm
Topic tested: DRAWING 2D SHAPES

Answers

5. 1 mark for both points and lines correct

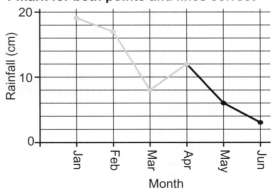

Topic tested: LINE GRAPHS

6. 1 mark for correct answer

*4 shares = 24 grapes,
so 1 share = 24 ÷ 4 = 6 grapes
Felix gets 5 shares = 5 × 6 = 30 grapes
Topic tested: UNEQUAL SHARING*

**7. 2 marks for correct answer
otherwise 1 mark for correct working**

*Felix spends £3.45 × 3 = £10.35
Anita spends £4.80 × 2 = £9.60
£10.35 − £9.60 = £0.75
Topic tested: CALCULATIONS WITH
MONEY*

Test 3 — pages 44-46

1. 1 mark for both correct

*Difference = 0.9 − 0.5 = 0.4
Next two terms:
1.3 + 0.4 = 1.7
1.7 + 0.4 = 2.1
Topic tested: SEQUENCES*

**2. 2 marks for the correct answer
otherwise 1 mark for correct working**

*46p ÷ 2 = 23p
72p × 3 = 216p
23p + 216p = 239p = £2.39
Topic tested: CALCULATIONS WITH
MONEY*

3. 1 mark for both correct

*13, 41
Topic tested: PRIME NUMBERS*

4. 1 mark

*2.15
Topic tested: NUMBER LINES*

5. 1 mark for correct answer

*Cricket bats = 30
Cricket balls = 25
30 − 25 = 5*

**1 mark for correct answer with
suitable explanation**

*NO
E.g.
There were 25 + 45 + 15 + 25 + 30 + 25
= 165 items sold in total, and 25 + 45 = 70
of those items were for table tennis. 70 is
less than half of 165, so Zac is not correct.
Topic tested: BAR CHARTS*

6. 1 mark

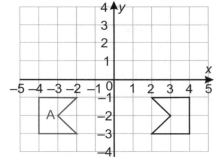

Topic tested: REFLECTION

**7. 2 marks for correct answer
otherwise 1 mark for correct working**

Split the shape up into two rectangles:

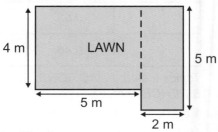

*5 × 4 = 20 m²
2 × 5 = 10 m²
20 + 10 = 30 m²
Topic tested: AREA*

Answers

Test 4 — pages 47-49

1. 1 mark

9°C
Topic tested: NEGATIVE NUMBERS

2. 1 mark for correct answer

£2.50 ÷ 2 = £1.25
£1.25 − 72p = 125p − 72p = 53p
Topic tested: CALCULATIONS WITH MONEY

3. 1 mark

29°
Topic tested: MEASURING ANGLES

4. 1 mark for all three statements correct

Its opposite angles are equal — true (✓)
It is called a parallelogram — true (✓)
It has four lines of symmetry — false (✗)

1 mark for correct answer

Area of a parallelogram = base × height
= 5 × 2 = 10 cm²
Topics tested: SHAPES & AREA

5. 1 mark for correct answer

6 × 2 = 12 tubes for 8 × 2 = 16 aeroplanes
6 ÷ 2 = 3 tubes for 8 ÷ 2 = 4 aeroplanes
so for 16 + 4 = 20 aeroplanes,
Felix needs 12 + 3 = 15 tubes of glue.
Topics tested: RATIO & PROPORTION

6. 1 mark for correct answer

1560 + 2440 = 4000 m = 4 km

1 mark for correct answer

5 miles ≈ 8 km, so 4 km ≈ 5 ÷ 2 = 2.5 miles
Topic tested: UNIT CONVERSIONS

7. 2 marks for correct answer
otherwise 1 mark for correct working

$\frac{1}{5}$ of 30 = 30 ÷ 5 = 6
so $\frac{2}{5}$ of 30 = 6 × 2 = 12
$\frac{1}{10}$ of 30 = 30 ÷ 10 = 3
so $\frac{3}{10}$ of 30 = 3 × 3 = 9
12 + 9 = 21 bottles sold in total,
so there are 30 − 21 = 9 bottles left.
Topic tested: FRACTIONS

Test 5 — pages 50-52

1. 1 mark for correct answer

750 − 736 = 14
766 − 750 = 16
So 736 is closer to 750
Topic tested: SUBTRACTION

2. 1 mark for both correct

B and E
Topic tested: 3D SHAPES

3. 1 mark for both correct multiples

Multiples of 8: 8, 16, 24, 32, 40, 48
Multiples of 12: 12, 24, 36, 48
So common multiples are 24 and 48
Topic tested: MULTIPLES

4. 1 mark for correct answer

25% of £280 = £280 ÷ 4 = £70
So 75% of £280 = £70 × 3 = £210
Topic tested: PERCENTAGES

5. 1 mark for correct answer

$\begin{array}{r} 2\;\;2\;r\,100 \\ 200\overline{)4\,5\,0^{50}0} \end{array}$
So the school will need to buy 23 boxes of paperclips.

1 mark for correct answer

$\begin{array}{r} 2\,.\,7\,0 \\ \times\qquad 8 \\ \hline £\,2\,1\,.\,6\,0 \\ {}^{5} \end{array}$

Topics tested: DIVISION & MULTIPLICATION

6. 1 mark

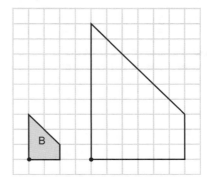

Topic tested: ENLARGEMENT

Answers

7. 1 mark for correct answer

6 + 5 + 4 = 15

1 mark for suitable explanation

E.g.

The graph shows that 8 children took between 6 and 8 minutes to walk to school, but Zac cannot tell how many of them took 6-7 minutes as the data is grouped.

Topic tested: BAR CHARTS

8. 1 mark for correct answer

$6^2 + (3 \times 6) = 36 + 18 = 54$

Topics tested: SQUARE NUMBERS & ALGEBRA

Arithmetic Test — pages 53-54

1. 1 mark

5943 + 100 = 6043

2. 1 mark

15.8 − 12 = 3.8

3. 1 mark

$2^3 = 8$

4. 1 mark

$$16\overline{)3\,{}^3\!8\,{}^6\!4}^{\;2\;4}$$

So 38.4 ÷ 16 = 24 ÷ 10 = 2.4

5. 1 mark

10% of 640 = 640 ÷ 10 = 64

5% of 640 = 64 ÷ 2 = 32

15% of 640 = 64 + 32 = 96

6. 1 mark

$1\frac{1}{5} - \frac{11}{10} = \frac{6}{5} - \frac{11}{10} = \frac{12}{10} - \frac{11}{10} = \frac{1}{10}$

7. 2 marks for correct answer
otherwise 1 mark for correct working

$$\begin{array}{r} 2\,9\,6\,2 \\ \times \quad 4\,7 \\ \hline 2\,0\,{}_6\!7\,{}_4\!3\,{}_1\!4 \\ 1\,1\,{}_3\!8\,{}_2\!4\,8\,0 \\ \hline 1\,3\,9\,2\,1\,4 \\ {}_1\;{}_1 \end{array}$$

8. 2 marks for correct answer
otherwise 1 mark for correct working

$$\begin{array}{r} 2\,3\,1 \\ 24\,\overline{)5\,5\,4\,4} \\ -\,4\,8 \\ \hline 7\,4 \\ -\,7\,2 \\ \hline 2\,4 \\ -\,2\,4 \\ \hline 0 \end{array}$$

Scoresheet Question — page 55

E.g.

2	9	4
7	5	3
6	1	8